WHO GOES TO SCHOOL?

MODERN CURRICULUM PRESS

WHO GOES TO SCHOOL?
Margaret Hillert
Illustrated by Nan Brooks

ISBN: 0-8136-5575-7
Printed in the United States of America

17 18 19 20 21 06 05 04 03

1-800-321-3106
www.pearsonlearning.com

Who goes to school?
Can you guess?
No, no.
You can not guess,
but you will see.

Look here.
Look at this.
This is a school.
A school for dogs.

The dog will sit.
The dog will walk.
The dog will go with you.
This is good.

Here is a school, too.
And here are big dogs.
See what the big dogs do.

This dog gets into a car.
This dog will work.
He will work with the man.

Here is a good dog.
See this dog work.
He is a big help.

The dog will go out.
He will look and look.
He will find something.

See this dog.
What can he do?
What is he good for?

This dog can work.
He can do good work.
He can help the man see.

And look at this little one.
What can he do?
Oh, look at this.

He did it!
He did it!
He is good.
What fun this is.

Here is a big baby.
It can do something, too.

It can sit up.

And here are big cats.
Big, big cats.

Cats at school.

The big cats sit.
The big cats play.
We like to see this.

Little cats go to school, too.
Look at this cat.
What a pretty one.

Now look at the TV.
Here is the little cat.
See what work she can do.
She is on TV.

This cat gets something.

She gets something little.
She is a big help.

This cat helps, too.
The man likes the cat.
What a good little cat.

Here is a school.
Boys and girls go to
this school.

Do you go to school, too?

Yes, you do.
You read.
You work.
You play, too.

You have fun here.
It is fun to go to school.

Margaret Hillert, author and poet, has written many books for young readers. She is a former first-grade teacher and lives in Birmingham, Michigan.

Who Goes to School? uses the 65 words listed below.

a
and
are
at

baby
big
boys
but

can
car
cat(s)

did
do
dog(s)

find
for
fun

gets
girls
go
goes
good
guess

have
he
help(s)
here

in
into
is
it

like(s)
little
look

man

no
not
now

oh
on
one
out

play
pretty

read

school
see
she
sit
something

the
this
to
too
TV

up

walk
we
what
who
will
with
work

yes
you